My First Day at School

By Emmi S. Herman
Pictures by Ruth J. Flanigan

Project Director: Judith E. Nayer • Creative Director: Jonette Jakobson

It was the first day of school. Mrs. Lee gave Amy
a big hug and a kiss in front of Room 103. "Have
a wonderful day, my shining star," said Mrs. Lee. She
showed Amy a folded piece of paper and quickly
put it in her daughter's pocket. "Open this in case
you need a little help."

Amy walked into the classroom. "Welcome to
Class 103," greeted a friendly lady. "You must be Amy.
I am your teacher, Mrs. Burns. Find your cubby
and then join the others on the rug."

Mrs. Burns walked off quickly. All of a sudden
Amy felt very alone. She reached inside her pocket
and touched the piece of paper her mother had put there.

"Amy, your cubby is next to mine," said a girl with red hair.

"Thank you," said Amy. She put her lunch box in a cubby marked "Amy" and the two girls walked over to the rug.

"Today we will meet new friends and learn names," said Mrs. Burns. One at a time she called out the children's names and put on name tags. The girl with the red hair got up. Her name was Katy. Amy waited and waited for her name to be called. She started to feel sad and remembered the piece of paper in her pocket.

"Amy Lee," called out Mrs. Burns. Amy got up quickly and quietly. Mrs. Burns put on Amy's name tag and smiled.

Then Mrs. Burns told the children about the activities for the morning. Amy chose block corner. But when she got there, three boys were already building a castle. There was no room for Amy, and she began to feel alone. Amy put her hand in her pocket and touched the paper.

"Do you want to help make a moat? Every castle needs a moat," said a boy named Ben.

"Okay," said Amy. She made a moat with Ben, Perry, and Gabriel.

When the principal came in to meet the children, she said it was the nicest moat she had ever seen.

Soon it was lunch time. "What a big, noisy place!" Amy thought.

Mrs. Burns spoke in an outdoor voice. "This is your table. You will sit here as a class the whole year. Children who eat hot lunch please follow me. The rest of my class may begin to eat now."

Amy looked for Katy but she could not find her.
She sat down at one end of the table. All around her
children were talking and laughing.

But Amy felt so alone she just stared at her lunch
box. Then Amy remembered the paper in her pocket.
She reached inside and felt it.

Just then Amy heard her name. It was Katy!
"May I sit here?" asked Katy, carrying a lunch tray.
"Sure," said Amy. "I was looking for you."
"I get hot lunch. I stand on that line over there,"
Katy said, pointing behind her.

Katy sat down and started to spread mustard on
her hamburger.

"You like mustard on your hamburger?" asked Amy.

"Yes, I do," answered Katy.

"So do I!" cheered Amy, and the two girls laughed.

After lunch, children ran in all directions in the yard. Amy couldn't decide what to do first. There were monkey bars, slides, two jungle gyms, tire swings, and seesaws.

"Can you give me a push?" asked a girl who was sitting on a tire swing.

"Okay," said Amy. So she pushed...and pushed...

…and pushed. Soon the girl was swinging very high.

"Wow!" giggled the girl. "You are good. What's your name?"

"Amy. What's yours?" Amy asked.

"Jenny," said the girl.

"Do you want to go on the monkey bars now?" asked Amy.

"Yes," answered Jenny. The girls raced to the monkey bars. But just as they got there Amy tripped and fell. She felt a stinging on her knees and then she saw the blood.

"Are you okay?" asked Jenny.

"No," said Amy, trying to hold back tears. Mrs. Burns walked over quickly. Jenny offered to take Amy to the nurse.

The school nurse washed Amy's knees and gave her a bandage for each.

"Last summer I fell and got stitches right here," said Jenny, pointing to the tip of her chin where a faint scar remained.

"Ugh!" said Amy, forgetting about her own injury. "Did it hurt?"

"Did it ever!" Jenny said dramatically.

After cool cups of water, the girls thanked the nurse and walked back to the classroom.

The children were sitting on the rug. Mrs. Burns smiled at the girls as they walked in. A few children asked what happened. Amy felt important telling her story and showing the bandages.

Soon it was time to go home. Amy saw her mother come into the classroom.

"There's my shining star," her mother said. "How did your first day go?"

Mrs. Burns came over to Mrs. Lee. "Amy fell in the yard but she was very brave. She had help from her friends."

"Did you need any other help?" asked Mrs. Lee, looking at Amy's pocket.

Amy's eyes widened. "So many things happened today, I didn't get a chance to open the piece of paper. Now I will!" exclaimed Amy, reaching into her pocket. She opened the paper and discovered a shining new star sticker.

Amy smiled and looked up at her mother. "I think
I was a shining star today without this after all!" she said.